IMPORTANT SAFETY
INSTRUCTIONS

While the **Publisher** has used all reasonable endeavours to ensure that these experiments are safe for children to undertake, there are some that require the **assistance of a grown-up**. These are marked with . . .

Young **bug-spotters**, please make use of your **grown-ups**, and don't try these alone! Stick to the steps in this book for **maximum safety** and the **best results**.

REMEMBER!

Always show **respect** to wild creatures and try **not to disturb** their environment. Some can **bite or sting**, so care should be taken at all times. If you are unsure, ask a grown-up for their help or advice.

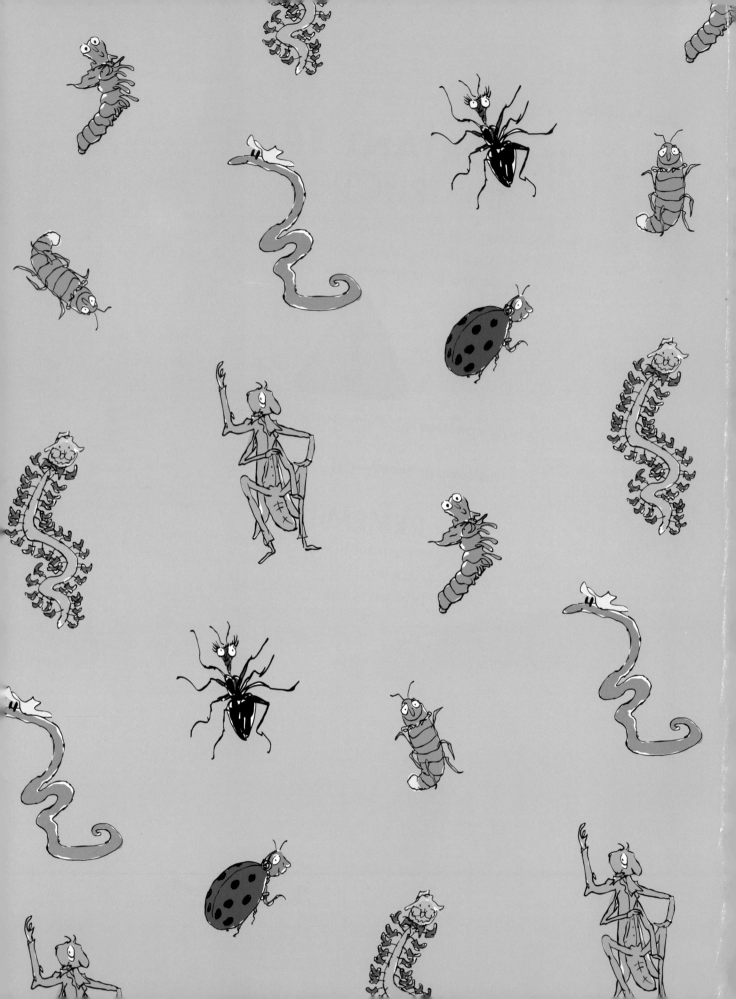

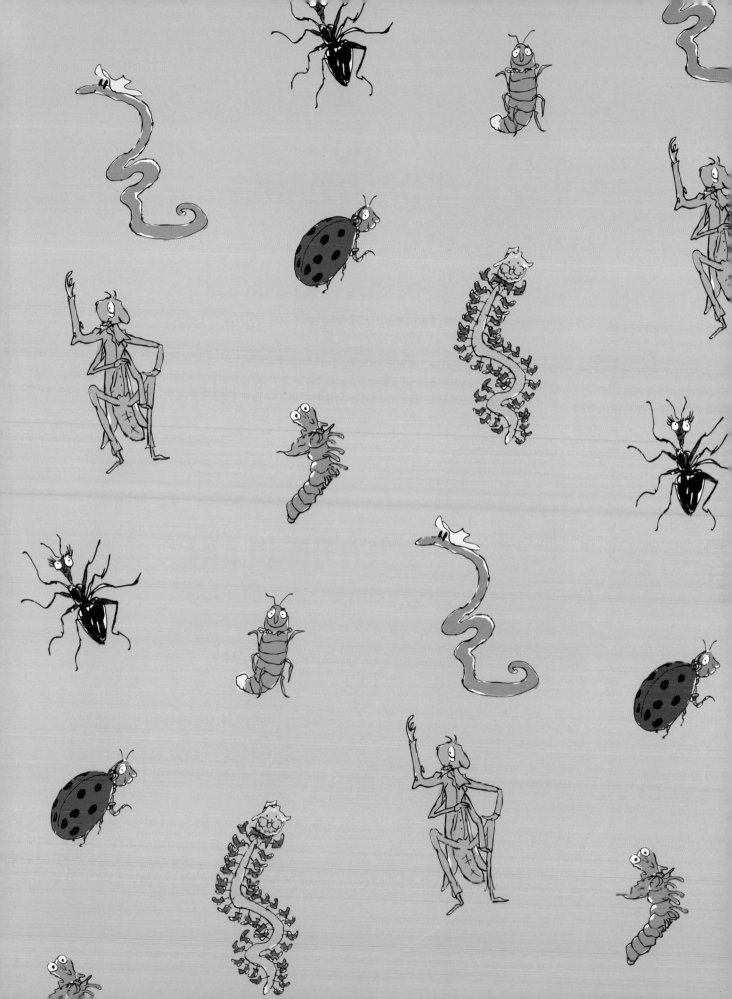

ROALD DAHL was a

spy, ace fighter pilot, chocolate historian and medical inventor. He was also the author of *Charlie and the Chocolate Factory, Matilda, The BFG* and many more brilliant stories. He remains **THE WORLD'S NUMBER ONE STORYTELLER.**

QUENTIN BLAKE

has illustrated more than three hundred books and was Roald Dahl's favourite illustrator. In 1980 he won the prestigious Kate Greenaway Medal. In 1999 he became the first ever Children's Laureate and in 2013 he was knighted for services to illustration.

ROALD DAHL'S

JAMES's GIANT BUG BOOK

Illustrated by QUENTIN BLAKE

PUFFIN

PUFFIN BOOKS

UK | USA | Canada | Ireland | Australia
India | New Zealand | South Africa

Puffin Books is part of the Penguin Random House group of companies
whose addresses can be found at global.penguinrandomhouse.com.

www.penguin.co.uk
www.puffin.co.uk
www.ladybird.co.uk

Penguin
Random House
UK

First published 2018

001

Written by Barry Hutchinson
Text copyright © Roald Dahl Nominee Ltd, 2018
Illustrations copyright © Quentin Blake, 2018
Diagrams by Jim Peacock

The moral right of the author and illustrators has been asserted

Thanks to Michelle Porte Davies

Printed in China

A CIP catalogue record for this book is available from the British Library

ISBN: 978–0–241–32221–5

All correspondence to:
Puffin Books
Penguin Random House Children's
80 Strand, London WC2R 0RL

MIX
Paper from
responsible sources
FSC® C018179

Penguin Random House is committed to a
sustainable future for our business, our readers
and our planet. This book is made from Forest
Stewardship Council® certified paper.

CONTENTS

INTRODUCTION

WELCOME to **James's Giant Bug Book**, inspired by Roald Dahl's *James and the Giant Peach*. In this marvellous tale, **James Henry Trotter** lives with his two horrid aunts, **Aunt Sponge** and **Aunt Spiker**.

JAMES is very lonely – until one day something peculiar happens. An **old man** gives him some little green seed-like things, and soon after, at the end of the garden, a peach starts to **grow and GROW AND GROW**. Inside that peach are seven very unusual and very **giant insects** – all waiting to take James on a magical adventure.

NOW, THIS BOOK might not explain the **mystery** of how James's bug friends got so **gigantic**, but it will take you on an adventure so **amazing** that by the end of it you'll become something of a **minibeast master**!

SO GET READY to embark on your own **giant bugtastic adventure**! You'll come face to face with some **fascinating creatures**, be **cleverly creative** and find yourself baffled by **cunning puzzles**!

DON'T FORGET!
James made friends with the bugs inside the Giant Peach by **being kind to them and showing them respect** – so make sure you do the same when you go on your own BUG ADVENTURES!

MEET THE CENTIPEDE

'My friends, this is the **Centipede**,
        and let me make it KNOWN
He is so sweet and GENTLE that
        (although he's OVERGROWN)
The **QUEEN OF SPAIN**, again and again,
        has summoned him by PHONE
To baby-sit and sing and knit
        and be a CHAPERONE
When nurse is off and all
        the **CHILDREN** are ALONE.'

'You have a lot of **boots**,' James murmured.

'I have a lot of **legs**,' the Centipede answered proudly. 'And a lot of feet. ONE HUNDRED, to be exact.'

*'**There** he goes again!'* the EARTHWORM cried, speaking for the first time. 'He simply cannot stop TELLING LIES about his legs! He doesn't have anything *like* a hundred of them! He's only got **forty-two!**'

The **Centipede** made a
WRIGGLING
movement with his body . . .

'**I am a pest!**' the Centipede announced, grinning broadly and looking round the room for approval.

THE ENCYCLO-CENTIPEDIA

James discovered many **fascinating facts** about the **Centipede**, and there's lots more you can find out too . . .

FANTASTIC FAMILY
They are part of the **myriapod family**, of which there are about **13,000 known species**.

FLATMATES
Centipedes have **flat bodies**.

HAVE A NICE TRIP
If you look closely, you'll see that the **legs towards the back** of a centipede are **longer** than the ones at the front – this helps **stop** them from **tripping over**!

ON YOUR MARKS . . .
Centipedes are **pretty speedy** and can **run very fast**.

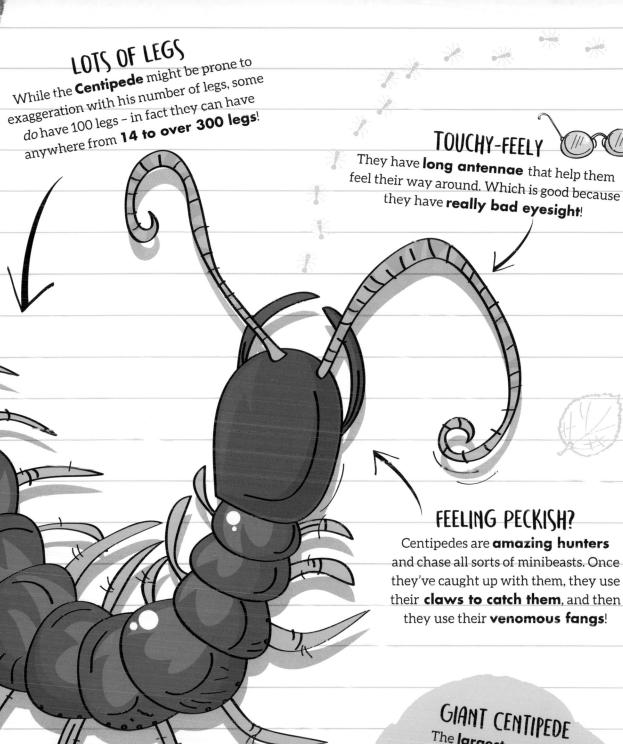

LOTS OF LEGS
While the **Centipede** might be prone to exaggeration with his number of legs, some do have 100 legs – in fact they can have anywhere from **14 to over 300 legs**!

TOUCHY-FEELY
They have **long antennae** that help them feel their way around. Which is good because they have **really bad eyesight**!

FEELING PECKISH?
Centipedes are **amazing hunters** and chase all sorts of minibeasts. Once they've caught up with them, they use their **claws to catch them**, and then they use their **venomous fangs**!

GIANT CENTIPEDE
The **largest species** of centipede is the **tropical giant centipede**, which can grow up to **30 centimetres long**, and lives in **northern South America**. It's so big it can catch mice, lizards, frogs and even bats in mid flight!

BREATHE IN
Although they have mouths, centipedes actually **breathe** through **tiny holes** in the **sides of their bodies**.

BUILD A BUG HOTEL

Although there are lots of **great places** for **centipedes** and **other bugs** to live in your garden, why not spoil them and build them a **Bug Hotel**?

DIFFICULTY RATING:

WHAT YOU'LL NEED:

- TWO-LITRE DRINKS BOTTLE
- SCISSORS
- TWIGS
- STICKS
- BAMBOO CANES
- DRINKING STRAWS
- STRING

1

Cut off the top and bottom of the drinks bottle, leaving a tube shape that's about **20 centimetres long**. You might need to get a grown-up to help you cut the bottle.

2 Gather together **twigs**, **sticks** and **bamboo canes** and place them **lengthways** in the bottle. Poke some **straws** in among everything – not only do they help to keep everything secure, some creepy crawlies will love chilling out in the straws too!

3 When the bottle is **full,** find a suitable **hedge** that you can **wedge it into**.

OR

Tie some string around the middle of the bottle and **hang your Bug Hotel** from a tree.

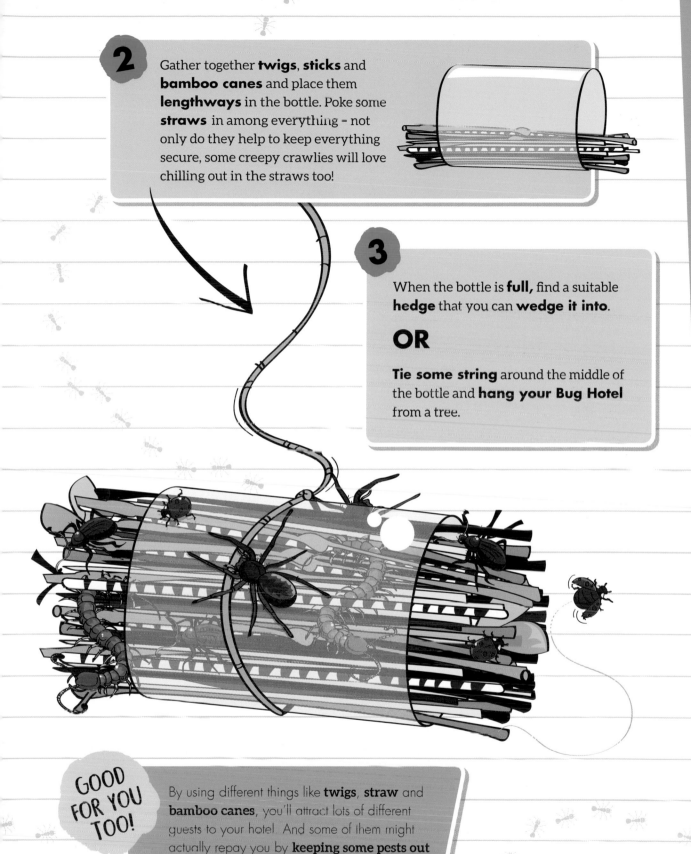

GOOD FOR YOU TOO!

By using different things like **twigs**, **straw** and **bamboo canes**, you'll attract lots of different guests to your hotel. And some of them might actually repay you by **keeping some pests out of your garden**. So make sure you keep an eye on your **Bug Hotel** to see who's checking in and who's checking out!

FAMILY FEUD

Although they are both long and wriggly with lots of legs and come from the **myriapod family**, you won't find centipedes and millipedes having fun family reunions. In fact, **centipedes hunt millipedes!** Here are some more **facts** about **millipedes** . . .

IN ONE END AND OUT THE OTHER

Underground, millipedes eat **dead plants** and **wood**, then they **poo** out new soil that in turn helps new plants grow!

DIG DEEP

Millipedes can't outrun centipedes because they are quite slow, but they have a clever way to escape – they **burrow underground!**

LOTS OF LEGS

Common species of millipede have between **80 and 400 legs**, although some rare species can have up to **750. Wow!**

AMAZING ACROBATICS

If millipedes entered the **insect Olympics** they'd definitely be gymnasts – their legs are so strong they can **climb trees** and **hang upside down**.

SPOT THE DIFFERENCE

If you're unsure whether you've found a centipede or a millipede, check out **how many legs** they have **per body segment** – millipedes have **two pairs of legs** per segment, but **centipedes** only have **one pair** per segment.

CHOOSE THE SHOES

'**James** worked away frantically on the **Centipede's boots**. Each one had **laces** that had to be untied and loosened before it could be pulled off, and to make matters worse, all the laces were tied up in the most **terrible complicated knots** that had to be unpicked with fingernails.'

The **Centipede** warned **James** that he should line up his boots **neatly in pairs** when he took them off. And with good reason! Look what happens when they just get thrown over your shoulder – they end up in a **confusing mess**! And to make matters worse, there's one **random boot** here too.

Can you **match the Centipede's boots into 21 pairs** and work out which boot **doesn't match** any of the others?

(Answer on page 83.)

ANT-STONISHING!

There's one insect that **wasn't aboard the Giant Peach** with James and you're bound to have seen it on your outdoor adventures. **Can you guess what it is?** It's an **ant**! Maybe next time James should think about inviting an ant along because they are pretty **awesome little critters** . . .

ANTZZZZZZ

Although ants always appear to be busy, **fire ants** can have around **250 sleeps per day**, although each one only lasts just over a minute.

HEAVY WEIGHT

In some parts of the world, it's estimated that ants make up about **25 per cent of the total biomass** (weight) of land-based animals – that's about the **same as humans!**

INSECT INVADERS

It is estimated that there are about **10,000 trillion ants** on **Earth**.

GI-ANTS

Ants range in size from **0.75 millimetres** to **52 millimetres**.

WEIGHTLIFTERS

Ants can carry an astounding **20 times their own weight** – that's like you lifting a **car**!

TWO TUMMIES

Ants have **two stomachs** – one for holding food for themselves and one for holding food for others. **It's good to share!**

MINI SOCIETY

Queen ants are the heads of ant colonies and lay thousands of eggs. **Male ants**, called **drones**, have one role, which is to mate with the queen. **Non-reproducing female ants** are called **workers** or **soldiers**, and they find food, care for the queen and offspring, build the nest, and defend the colony or attack others.

DID YOU KNOW?

Ants and humans are the only animals that **farm other creatures**! Some ants protect aphids from other predators, and in return the aphids provide the ants with nectar or honeydew that they've gathered from plants.

OLD-AGED INSECTS

Queen ants can live for up to **30 years** – that's the longest of any insect.

MILLION TO ONE

There are roughly **1 million ants** for every **human** on Earth.

OUCH!

Of all insects, **bullet ants** from **South America** are said to have the most **painful sting** and it can last for a whole day!

MARCHING BOOTS

Foraging worker ants can travel up to **200 metres from their nest** in search of food.

AWESOME ANT FARM

WHAT YOU'LL NEED:
- SOIL AND SAND
- BOWL OR BUCKET
- LARGE GLASS JAR WITH LID
- SMALL GLASS JAR WITH LID THAT WILL FIT INSIDE YOUR LARGE JAR WITH ABOUT 1–2 CENTIMETRES AROUND THE EDGE
- FUNNEL OR SPOON, SKEWER AND TROWEL
- JAM, FRUIT OR SUGAR SOLUTION
- 20–25 FRIENDLY ANTS
- BLACK CARD
- STICKY TAPE OR DOUBLE-SIDED TAPE

Just like James and his friends on their adventure, **ants work together** to survive. By building your own **ant farm** you can observe the teamwork of your own colony of ants.

DID YOU KNOW?

It's easy to make **sugar solution**. **Dissolve sugar** in **hot water** and then leave it to cool. Be careful when handling hot water; you will need a grown-up to help.

> ! Be careful, though, **ants can bite and sting**, so either **wear thick gardening gloves** when handling ants or ask a **grown-up to help you**.

DIFFICULTY RATING:

1

Mix the **soil** with the **sand** in a bowl or bucket. You want about **two-thirds soil** to **one-third sand**.

2

Place the small jar with its lid on inside the large jar, and **carefully** fill the gap between the two jars with your soil and sand mixture. Use a funnel or a spoon to avoid mess. Fill it up until there's about **2 centimetres** of the smaller jar still showing.

3

Ask a grown-up to make some **small holes in the lid** of the larger jar using something sharp like a skewer. Make sure that they are small enough so that your ants can't escape.

4

Have a look **under stones or rocks** and collect your ants from an outdoor colony. Make sure you get them from the **same place**, as ants from different colonies don't usually get on! **Some ants bite**, so it might be best to use a trowel and ask a grown-up to help.

5 **Carefully** put your ants inside your ant farm. To keep them happy you could place some **food** (like jam, some fruit or sugar solution) on the **lid of the smaller jar**. Then screw on the larger lid.

6

Make a **tube of card** large enough to fit **snugly around the large jar** using sticky tape. Place it in a warm room out of direct sunlight and let your ants get to work!

REMEMBER TO PUT ME BACK IN THE WILD!

TOP TIP!

Ants get most of their **water from their food**, but if the soil mixture is looking particularly dry, **soak some cotton wool** in water and place it on the lid of the small jar. **Don't pour water directly into the jar** as this could drown your ants.

DID YOU KNOW?

Not only does the smaller jar provide a **feeding station**, it also encourages the ants to build their tunnels against the side of the larger jar so that you can see them at work!

MEET THE EARTHWORM

'The **Earthworm**, on the other hand,'
Said **James**, beginning to expand,
'Is great for **DIGGING** up the land
And making old soils newer.
Moreover, you should UNDERSTAND
He would be absolutely GRAND
For digging **SUBWAY TUNNELS** and
For making you a **SEWER**.'

'In my opinion,' the **Earthworm** said, 'the *really* marvellous thing is to have **NO LEGS** at all and to be ABLE TO WALK just the same.'

'You call that **walking**?' cried the Centipede.

'I glide,' said the EARTHWORM primly.

'You are a slimy beast,' answered the Centipede.

'I am **NOT** a **SLIMY BEAST**,' the Earthworm said. 'I am a **USEFUL** and **MUCH LOVED CREATURE**. Ask any gardener you like. ... Next time you stand in a field or in a garden and look around you, then just remember this: that EVERY GRAIN OF SOIL upon the surface of the land, every tiny little bit of soil that you can see has actually PASSED THROUGH THE BODY OF AN EARTHWORM during the last few years!'

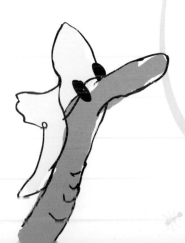

WHAT ON EARTHWORMS!

Another really **marvellous thing** about **worms** is that they have **no legs**, yet they still manage to get around. But that's just the beginning of the wonderful world of worms . . .

BODY TALK

Earthworms have **soft bodies** made up of segments, with a **head at one end** and something called a **saddle somewhere in the middle**! The **head** is at the more **pointy** end, and the **tail** is at the **rounder**, fatter end. The saddle is usually closer to the head than to the tail.

HAPPY B-EARTH-DAY!
Worms can **live** for up to **10 years**.

HEAD

SADDLE

DEAD FUSSY

Earthworms aren't very fussy and will **eat almost anything** that was alive, as long as it's **dead before** they get munching.

FEELING FULL

Earthworms can **eat** their **own body weight** in food every day.

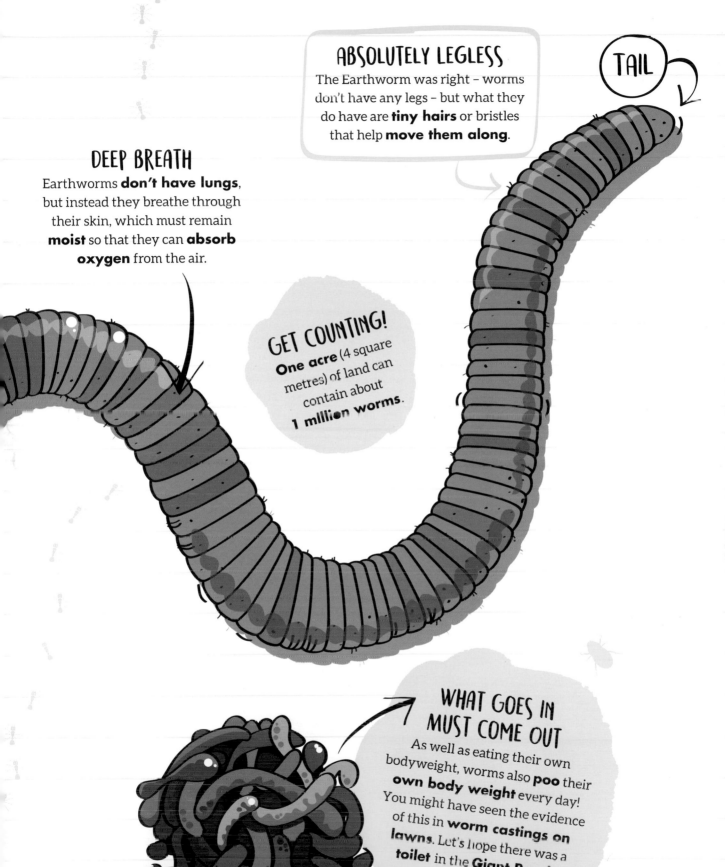

ABSOLUTELY LEGLESS

The Earthworm was right – worms don't have any legs – but what they do have are **tiny hairs** or bristles that help **move them along**.

TAIL

DEEP BREATH

Earthworms **don't have lungs**, but instead they breathe through their skin, which must remain **moist** so that they can **absorb oxygen** from the air.

GET COUNTING!
One acre (4 square metres) of land can contain about **1 million worms**.

WHAT GOES IN MUST COME OUT

As well as eating their own bodyweight, worms also **poo** their **own body weight** every day! You might have seen the evidence of this in **worm castings on lawns**. Let's hope there was a **toilet** in the **Giant Peach**!

17

WORM FARM FUN!

James, the **Earthworm** and all the other insects ended up munching on the **Giant Peach** when they felt hungry, but earthworms eat a lot more than just peaches. Have a go at building your own **worm farm** to see what they like to feast on.

DIFFICULTY RATING:

WHAT YOU'LL NEED:

- CLEAR PLASTIC BOX, ABOUT 20CM X 20CM X 20CM
- MOIST SOIL
- SAND
- OLD, DEAD LEAVES
- VEGETABLE PEELINGS, OVERRIPE FRUIT, TEA LEAVES
- 2 OR 3 EARTHWORMS EAGER FOR A HOLIDAY
- CLING FILM
- LARGE ELASTIC BAND
- BLACK CARD AND STICKY TAPE

1 Start by putting a **1-centimetre-deep layer of soil** at the bottom of your plastic box. Then **add a layer of sand** about 1 centimetre deep. **Repeat** this process, **alternating** between soil and sand until there is a space of about **5 centimetres left at the top**.

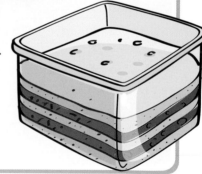

2 **Add a layer of leaves**, followed by vegetable peelings, overripe fruit and tea leaves.

Add your worms!

3

Place some **cling film over the top** and secure it in place with an **elastic band** – this will stop your worms from wriggling out! Don't forget to **poke some air holes** in the cling film so that the worms can breathe.

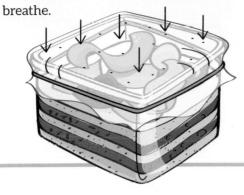

4

Use **black card** and sticky tape to make a **'jacket'** that fits snugly round the box – worms don't like the light! **Don't make it too tight**, though; you want to be able to slide it off.

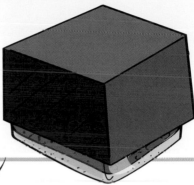

5

Put the box somewhere **cool and dark**. **Check every day** to see whether your worms have eaten the food and to look at the patterns they've made using the soil and sand. **Make sure you keep the soil nice and moist by adding water.**

TOP TIP!

The **Earthworm** liked eating the **Giant Peach**, so why not try feeding your worms some peach too?

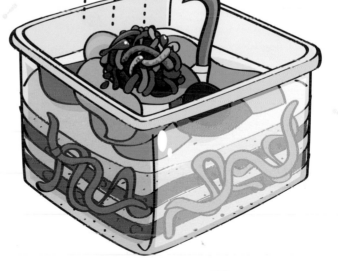

REMEMBER TO PUT ME BACK IN THE WILD!

WOWZA WORMS!

Unlike the Earthworm in the Giant Peach, **most earthworms grow to about 7 or 8 centimetres** in length. However, one worm found in **Widnes** in north-west England in 2016 wowed the experts at the Natural History Museum because it measured an amazing **40 centimetres** – it would stretch across two pages of this book. It weighed about **40 grams**, the same as a **small chocolate bar**. The people who found this wonderful worm named him **Dave**!

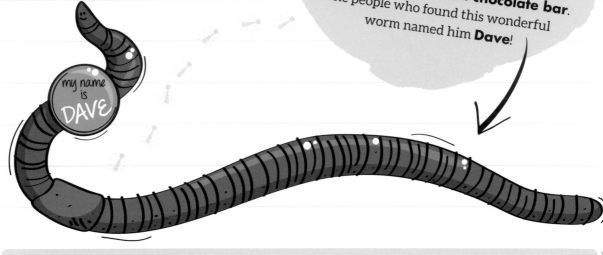

my name is DAVE

However, Dave is nothing compared to the **African giant earthworm**. This not-so-minibeast is part of the same family as the earthworms you might find in your garden or at the park – the **microchaetidae family** – but it's bigger. **A lot bigger**.

The African giant earthworm averages **1.36 metres in length** – which is about the **height of a nine-year-old child**! However, they can reach up to **6.7 metres** – that's about as long as **one and a half London black-cab taxis**! **And they can weigh 1.5 kilograms!**

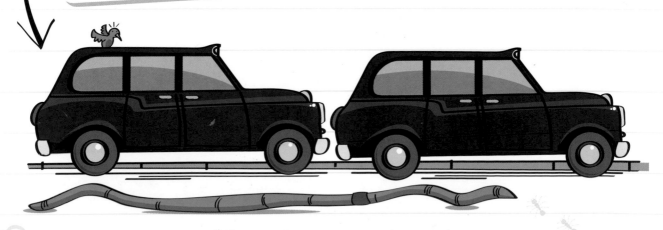

WORM YOUR WAY OUT OF THIS!

The Earthworm was the most concerned of all the insects about eating the **Giant Peach**. He thought it was a crazy idea to eat their ship as it was the only thing keeping them from drowning. James eventually persuaded him that there was enough peach to **eat AND sail in**!

Can you work out which of these earthworms is munching the peach?

(Answer on page 83.)

SNAILED IT!

James and his friends made their home in the Giant Peach – but imagine being able to carry your house around with you on your back! Well, there's a **minibeast** that you'll find lurking in most gardens that does just that . . .

MAGNIFICENT MOLLUSCS
Snails are part of the **mollusc family** which also includes **shellfish, octopuses and squids**.

EYE, EYE
On the end of the **longer tentacles**, you'll find a **snail's eyes**; the lower, smaller tentacles help them feel their way around.

DID YOU KNOW?
Almost all snail shells **spiral in a clockwise** direction from the centre.

TERRIFIC TEETH
Most snails have a **ribbon-like tongue** called a **radula**, which contains thousands of **tiny teeth**. It works by ripping food into little pieces.

A SNAIL'S PACE
Snails are one of the **slowest creatures on Earth**. Common garden snails have a top speed of **45 metres per hour**.

NO WAY!
Did you know that snails have feet? Well, technically each snail has one foot underneath its body. A band of muscles contracts and expands to create a rippling movement that propels the snail forward.

3 Find somewhere **dark and damp in your garden** or park, preferably where you have seen snails or snail trails previously, and set down the old plate or saucer. **Pour some of the solution** from the jug on to the plate or saucer. **Don't** add too much as you don't want your snails to drown.

4 **Check back at regular intervals** until you have gathered enough snails for your race.

5 Place the snails at the **start of your racetrack** and **watch them go**! This part could take some time . . .

TOP TIP!

You could try encouraging your snails by putting **food along the racetrack**!

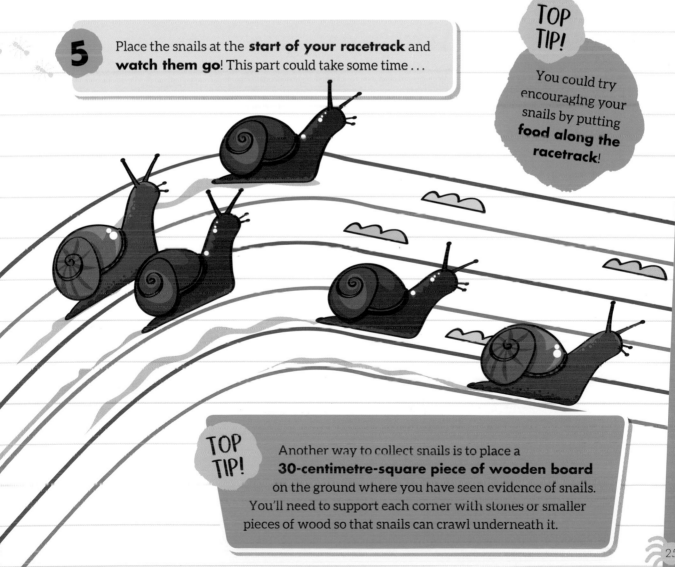

TOP TIP! Another way to collect snails is to place a **30-centimetre-square piece of wooden board** on the ground where you have seen evidence of snails. You'll need to support each corner with stones or smaller pieces of wood so that snails can crawl underneath it.

MEET THE GRASSHOPPER

'And the **Grasshopper**, ladies and gents, is a boon
In **MILLIONS** and **MILLIONS** of ways.

You have only to ask him to give you a TUNE
And he **PLAYS** and he **PLAYS** and he **PLAYS**.

As a toy for your children he's perfectly sweet;
There's nothing so good in the shops –
You've only to **tickle** the soles of his feet
And he **HOPS**
            and he **HOPS**
                        and he **HOPS** ;'

An **INSECT** is usually something rather small, is it not? A **grasshopper**, for example, is an insect.

There was an **OLD-GREEN-GRASSHOPPER** as large as a large dog sitting directly across the room from James now.

'I am the **ONLY PEST** in this room!' cried the **Centipede**, still grinning away. 'Unless you count OLD-GREEN-GRASSHOPPER over there. But he is long past it now. He is too old to be a pest any more.'

The Old-Green-Grasshopper turned his huge black eyes upon the Centipede and gave him a **WITHERING LOOK**. 'Young fellow,' he said, speaking in a deep, slow, scornful voice, 'I have never been a pest in my life. **I AM A MUSICIAN.**'

GREAT GRASSHOPPERS

TWO SETS OF WINGS

The **Old-Green-Grasshopper** told James all about his **musical skills**, including the difference between the way he and other **short-horned** grasshoppers make music compared to **long-horned** species. However, there's so much more that the Old-Green-Grasshopper can be proud of . . .

MASTERS OF DISGUISE
They are often coloured in a way that helps to camouflage them in their habitat, so you'll find green ones in fields and sandy-coloured ones in deserts.

ABDOMEN

CRAZY CATAPULTS
The grasshopper's back legs are a bit like **miniature catapults**. As it bends its legs at the knee, it **stores up energy like a spring**. When it is ready to jump, it relaxes the leg muscles, the 'spring' releases and the grasshopper is catapulted into the air.

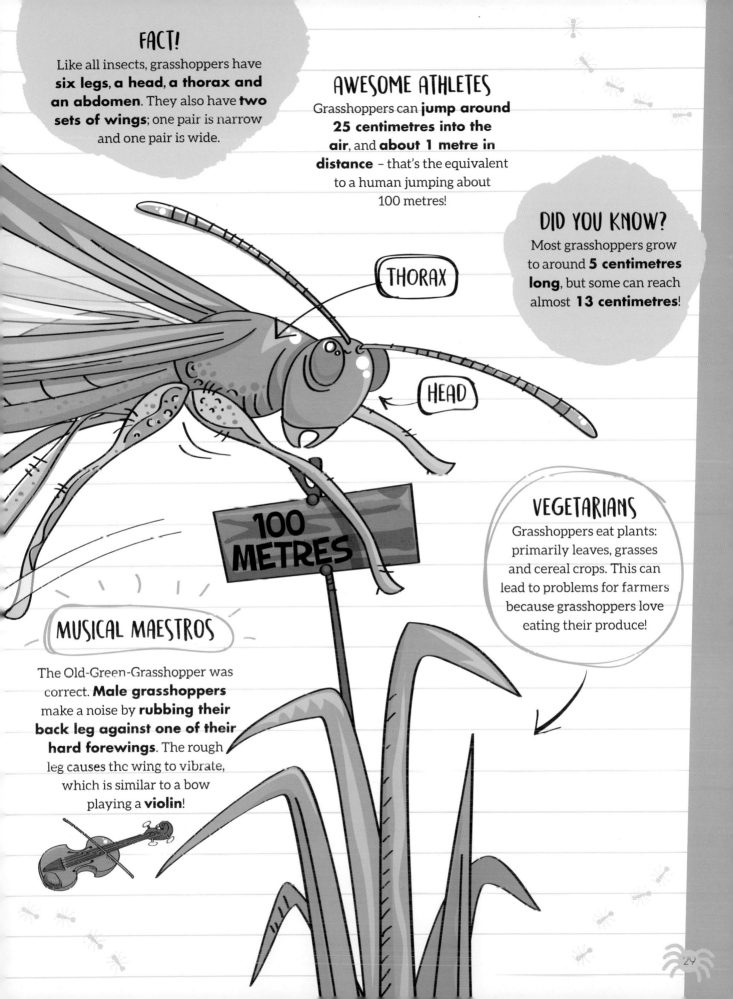

FACT!

Like all insects, grasshoppers have **six legs, a head, a thorax and an abdomen**. They also have **two sets of wings**; one pair is narrow and one pair is wide.

AWESOME ATHLETES

Grasshoppers can **jump around 25 centimetres into the air**, and **about 1 metre in distance** – that's the equivalent to a human jumping about 100 metres!

DID YOU KNOW?

Most grasshoppers grow to around **5 centimetres long**, but some can reach almost **13 centimetres**!

THORAX

HEAD

100 METRES

VEGETARIANS

Grasshoppers eat plants: primarily leaves, grasses and cereal crops. This can lead to problems for farmers because grasshoppers love eating their produce!

MUSICAL MAESTROS

The Old-Green-Grasshopper was correct. **Male grasshoppers** make a noise by **rubbing their back leg against one of their hard forewings**. The rough leg causes the wing to vibrate, which is similar to a bow playing a **violin**!

29

MUSIC MAKER

WHAT YOU'LL NEED:
- 1 SIX-EGG CARTON
- SCISSORS
- GREEN PAINT
- PENCIL
- GREEN CARD
- EMERY BOARD
- 2 SMALL GREEN POM-POMS
- PVA GLUE
- 2 GOOGLY EYES
- GREEN PIPE CLEANER
- CRAFT STICK

From the moment the Old-Green-Grasshopper started playing his music, the **audience were spellbound**. He made **beautiful sounds** by stroking the top of his hind leg up and down against his wing.

Here's how to make your own **musical grasshopper** at home!

DIFFICULTY RATING:

1

Cut your egg carton in half so that you have **three compartments in a row**: this is going to be your grasshopper's long body. **Paint it green** and set it aside to dry.

2

Next, it's time to make your grasshopper's large hind legs. **Draw a V on the green card**; you want **each outer line of the V to be 10 centimetres long and 1.5 centimetres wide**. When you are happy with your shape, cut it out using scissors. You can then use this first hind leg as a **template** for the second one by drawing around it on the card. Then cut out the second one. Make sure you are careful when using scissors, and ask a grown-up to help you.

3

Using scissors, **carefully cut the emery board in half**; you might need to ask a grown-up to help you with this. Then take one of your legs and **turn the V upside down. Glue one piece of the emery board to the right-hand part of one of the Vs**. Do the same for the second leg, but glue the emery board to the **left-hand part of the V**.

4

When the **paint on the body is dry, glue the pom-poms to the front**, and then **glue the googly eyes to the pom-poms**. Finally, make the **pipe cleaner into a U shape** and poke the ends through the front section of the carton, behind the eyes, giving your grasshopper antennae.

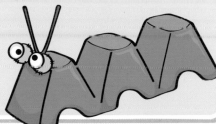

5

Glue the hind legs to the back section of the egg carton: one on each side. When the glue has dried, use the craft stick to rub along the emery board on the leg to make a noise.

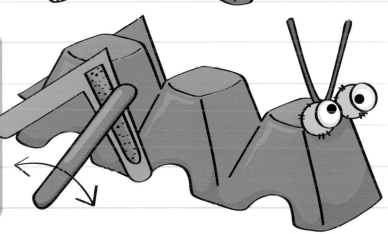

TOP TIP!
If you don't have any craft sticks, you could use a **pencil, a twig** or even a **chopstick**!

GET CREATIVE!
If you're feeling arty, decorate your grasshopper.

ANYONE FOR CRICKETS?

The **Old-Green-Grasshopper** didn't speak very highly of his relative, the **cricket**, referring to the species as **wing-rubbers** because of the way they make sounds. However, he did let on that they have **ears in their front legs**, just below the knees. If you think that's amazing, check out these facts!

DID YOU KNOW?
Crickets have long thin antennae, whereas a grasshopper's are short.

WHAT'S THE RUB?
Male crickets do indeed make noise by **rubbing their wings together**. Females are attracted to males that make the **loudest 'song'**.

FAMILY TIES
Crickets, like grasshoppers, are part of the **caelifera family**.

HEAR! HEAR!
It's true – crickets really do **listen with their legs**, whereas grasshoppers hear with their abdomen!

MUNCH
Crickets are omnivores, eating both plants and other animals.

NIGHTY-NIGHT
Crickets are nocturnal, meaning that they are active at night. **Grasshoppers**, on the other hand, are active during the day, which is known as **diurnal**.

HIDING HOPPER

At first it was difficult for **James** to see the **Cloud-Men** because they were as white as the clouds they were hiding in, but eventually he was able to make out the **tall, wispy, wraith-like, shadowy, white creatures** who looked as though they were made out of a mixture of cotton wool and candyfloss and thin white hairs.

It can be just as difficult to **spot a grasshopper** in a garden or park. You'll probably **hear them first**, but as soon as you get close they become silent. See if you can **spot** the **grasshopper hiding among these plants**.

(Answer on page 83.)

WEIRD AND WONDERFUL
WOODLICE

HOME, SWEET HOME

If you look under a flowerpot, you might come across a woodlouse because they **love damp, dark places** and **feeding on old rotting plants**.

The **Giant Peach** came **under attack** in the story, and the friends had to work out all sorts of ways to **defend** themselves. However, there's one little insect that is often found in gardens and woodland that has its own perfect protection – the **woodlouse** with its **amazing shell**! Read on for some more **wacky woodlice facts**!

WOW!

There are lots of different names for these little bugs, including **pea-bugs**, **chiggy pigs**, **armadillo bugs** and **roll-up bugs**. Which is your favourite?

GET COUNTING!

If you look closely, you'll see that woodlice have **seven pairs of legs**.

GIVE US A WAVE!

As they go about their business, woodlice are **constantly waving their feelers**. This is to help them get around in the dark.

DID YOU KNOW?

These minibeasts aren't actually insects at all. In fact, they are **more closely related to crabs, lobsters and shrimps**!

PERFECT PROTECTION

Some woodlice **curl into a ball when they are threatened**, and their armoured backs provide them with protection.

LOUSE HOUSE

Aunt Sponge and **Aunt Spiker** lived in a queer ramshackle house on the top of a hill in the **south of England**, but by all accounts it wasn't a very welcoming house, and James definitely didn't enjoy living there.

However, here's a **house** that you can make that is much more inviting – at least it will be to a **woodlouse!**

DIFFICULTY RATING: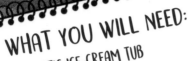

WHAT YOU WILL NEED:

- PLASTIC ICE-CREAM TUB WITH ITS LID
- DAMP SOIL
- SMALL LUMP OF WOOD OR TREE BARK
- DEAD LEAVES
- SKEWER OR KNITTING NEEDLE
- 2 OR 3 ADVENTUROUS WOODLICE
- WATER MIST SPRAYER

1 Make sure that you have **cleaned your ice-cream tub** and then **add damp soil to a depth of about 2 centimetres**.

2 Place the **lump of wood or tree bark** on the soil – **woodlice love to hide** under this kind of thing in the wild.

3 **Scatter the dead leaves** around the box so that you **cover all the remaining soil**. It's a good idea to use different varieties of leaf so that your woodlice don't get bored!

4 Using the **skewer**, make some **air holes in the lid** of the ice-cream tub. If you don't have a skewer, you could use something like a knitting needle. Be careful not to hurt yourself; **you might need to ask a grown-up for help**.

5 Carefully **place your woodlice** in their new home.

TOP TIP!

Check in on your woodlice **daily** and give them a **light spray of water** to maintain the moisture.

REMEMBER TO PUT ME BACK IN THE WILD!

6 Using the mister, **spray some water** into the tub and then **put the lid on securely**.

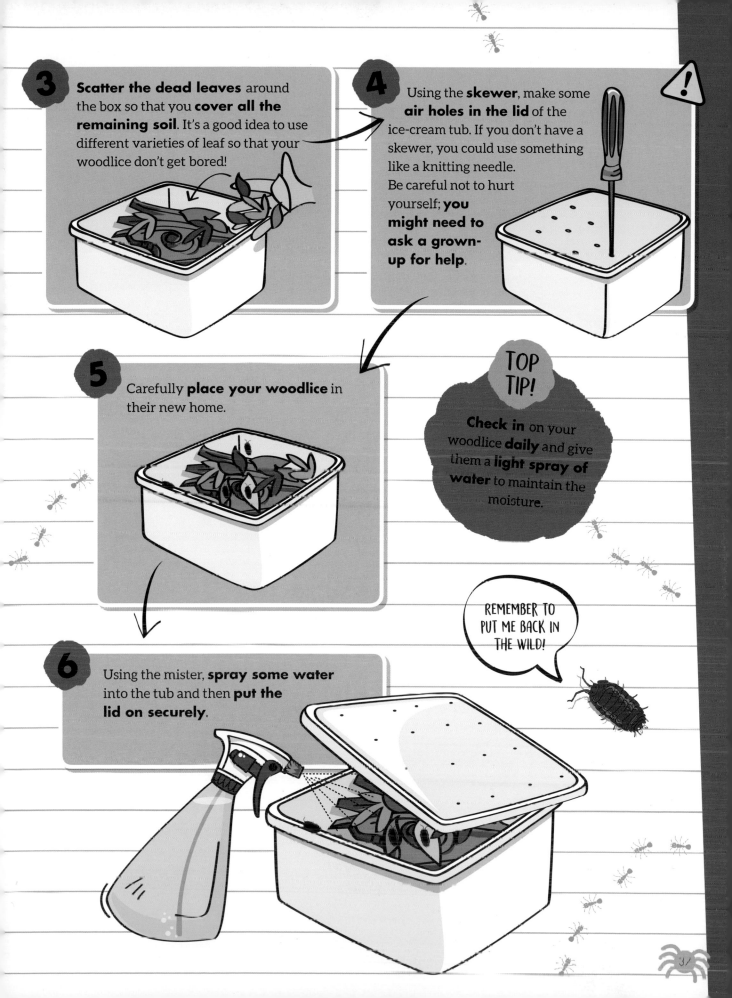

There was a **giant** LADYBIRD with nine black spots on her scarlet shell.

'. . . we **gobble** up all the NASTY little insects that are gobbling up the farmer's crops. It helps ENORMOUSLY, and we ourselves don't charge a penny for our services.'

'Oh, my goodness, THE POOR THING!' the **Ladybird** cried. 'I do believe he thinks it's *him* that we are wanting to eat!'

There was a **ROAR OF LAUGHTER** from all sides.

'Oh dear, oh dear!' they said. 'What an **AWFUL** thought!'

'You mustn't be frightened,' the Ladybird said kindly. 'We wouldn't *dream* of hurting you. You are one of *us* now, didn't you know that? You are **ONE OF THE CREW**. We're all in the same boat.'

SPOT ON!

...were gathering in gardens. It's time to find out some more about these **colourful little creatures!**

BIRDS OR BUGS

Another name for ladybirds is **ladybugs.**

CLEVER!

Ladybirds' shells aren't just for **decoration**; they send a **message to predators** that they may **taste bad** or even be **poisonous**.

TASTY

Ladybirds use their **antennae** to **taste and smell**.

COLOURFUL CRITTERS

Ladybirds **don't just come in red**; their shells can be other colours, including **yellow and orange**, or even **black with red spots**! They might have two, seven, twelve or even more spots.

KEEP WARM!

During the winter, ladybirds **hibernate together** to keep warm. You might cvcn find some asleep in your house in the colder months.

DID YOU KNOW?

Ladybirds can fly! Underneath their shiny, colourful backs are **two folded wings**. The shells are actually a set of wings too, but they don't use them for flying.

LADIES AND GENTS

Although they are called ladybirds, you do get **male** and **female** ladybirds!

DON'T TOUCH!

Ladybirds use a **variety of tactics to defend themselves**, including **playing dead** and oozing a **yellow fluid that predators find stinky!** Maybe the Ladybird should have tried this on the Cloud-Men!

TUMBLE TRAP!

It was the **Ladybird** who told **James** that the **Giant Peach** was about to tumble down the hill, leading to their **fantastic adventure**. Here's something you can make for all sorts of bugs to tumble into, not just ladybirds, so that you can observe them! It's called a **Tumble Trap**.

DIFFICULTY RATING

CHECK! Make sure you check with whoever looks after your garden before you dig up any soil. Ask them to help you find the best spot.

1 Using the **trowel, dig a hole in your garden** that's large enough for your yogurt pot. **Somewhere shady** is good.

2 Place your yogurt pot in the hole and **fill in any gaps**, around the edge.

3 Put the **insect food in the yogurt pot**. This is **bait to lure in some insects**. You could try one type of food at a time to see if different bait attracts different bugs.

4 Place the **slate, tile or flat piece of wood over the yogurt pot**, setting a stone under each corner so that your insects can get into the trap. The slate, tile or wood **provides a 'lid'** so that rain can't get inside.

5 **Go away and wait for insects to arrive.** Check back every few hours as your bugs won't be able to escape. When you've observed what insects are in the trap, you can then **release them back into the wild**.

TOP TIP!

You could try out other types of bait too – how about a small piece of your favourite chocolate bar, fruit or a piece of cooked meat?

BRILLIANT BEETLES!

When **James** introduced the **Ladybird** to the people of **New York**, he told them about her **400 children**, but what he didn't mention was that she's part of the **beetle family**, and that is huge! In fact, there are around **350,000 known species of beetle!**

DID YOU KNOW?

Just like the ladybird, **the front pair of wings on all beetles is hardened into wing cases**, known as **elytra**, which distinguish them from most other insects.

DID YOU KNOW?

The **giraffe stag beetle from India** can grow to around **10 centimetres long**.

Most stag beetles in Great Britain are about 5 centimetres long.

WOW!

Stag beetles have jaws, known as **mandibles**, that have evolved to look a bit like stag antlers.

AMAZING!

Stag beetles are a group of about 1,200 species of beetle in the family **Lucanidae**.

NO PLACE LIKE HOME

Stag beetles spend most of their time in and around rotting logs. You can encourage stag beetles by building a **woodpile**. In fact, some parks and nature reserves have them just so that stag beetles can set up home!

BIG MOUTH

Some stag beetles have **jaws as big as their bodies**, which can make getting around quite tricky.

SPOT THE DIFFERENCE

The **Ladybird** had **nine black spots** on her scarlet shell, but in these **two pictures** there are all sorts of different ladybirds. Can you **spot the eight differences** between the pictures?

[Answers on page 83.]

45

SHAPE-SHIFTER

LIFE CYCLE

The life cycle of a butterfly has **four stages**: egg, caterpillar, pupa and adult (when it eventually looks like a butterfly).

The **little green things** that the old man gave James might have had an astonishing enlarging effect on the bugs and the peach in **Aunt Sponge** and **Aunt Spiker's garden**, but there's a **minibeast** that can transform in an even more fantastic way. It's time to meet . . . the **butterfly**!

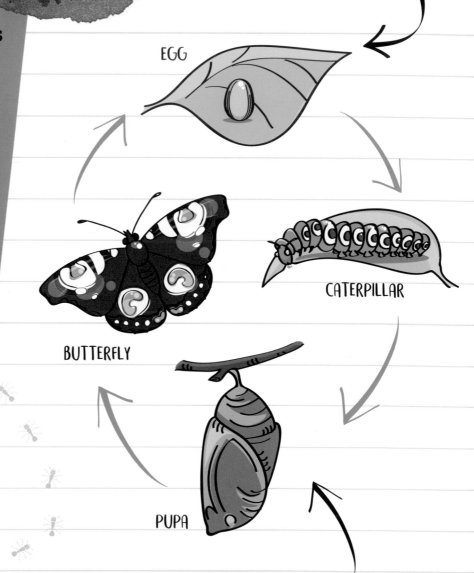

EGG

CATERPILLAR

BUTTERFLY

PUPA

CRAZY CHRYSALIS

When a **caterpillar has reached its full size**, it sheds its skin to reveal a new body called a **prepupa**. It then **spins silk** and attaches itself to a branch. Next, its **body hardens to form a chrysalis**. Inside the chrysalis a **crazy transformation occurs** until the butterfly is ready to break out.

HAPPY FLAPPERS

Skippers are the fastest butterflies. They can travel at around **37 miles per hour** or 60 kilometres per hour!

TASTY!

Butterflies use their **front feet to taste**!

TONGUE-TIED

A butterfly's tongue is called a proboscis. It uses this to sip its food, including flower nectar and tree sap, neither of which sounds too bad. However, **some butterflies drink from animal droppings** – yuck!

FEELING HUNGRY

Adult butterflies think ahead and make sure that they lay their eggs on a plant the caterpillar will want to eat once it's hatched. **Caterpillars are very hungry**, and as they eat they shed their old skin because they get too big for it! Imagine if humans did that!

DID YOU KNOW?

The colour on butterfly wings is made from **thousands of tiny scales**.

CLEVER CAMOUFLAGE

Both adult butterflies and caterpillars use a variety of techniques to protect themselves from predators. These include **camouflage** and **eye spots** so that they look like larger creatures, and **some caterpillars are even patterned like snakes**!

WOW!

The **morpho butterfly** from Central and South America has a **wingspan of up to 15 centimetres!**

BUTTERFLY FEEDER

With the **Giant Peach** floating in the sea, the **Centipede** and the **Earthworm** were unusually in agreement when they feared they might **starve to death**. Luckily James came up with a solution when he suggested that they **eat the Giant Peach**.

Sometimes **insects** in your garden need a bit of help when it comes to finding food too. This **feeding station** is perfect for **peckish butterflies**.

DIFFICULTY RATING:

1 ⚠️ Screw the **metal eyes** into the **four corners of the plywood**. You might need to ask a grown-up to help you with this.

2 **Cut your piece of string in half** so that you have two pieces that are each 1 metre long. Then carefully **thread one of the pieces through two of the metal eyes and tie a knot so that you have a loop**. Repeat with the second piece of string and the other two metal eyes.

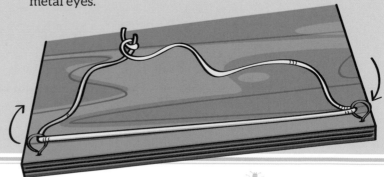

3 Place your jam-jar lids on the coloured card and **draw a circle around them**. Draw **flower petals around these circles** and carefully cut them out using scissors. You might need to ask a grown-up to help you with this. Once you have cut out your flowers, **stick the jam-jar lids on each piece of card**.

4 Hang the plywood from a suitable tree branch using the loops of string. Try to get the feeding table **as flat as possible** by adjusting the loops to help you do this. You might need to ask a grown-up to help you. When you have done this, place the jam-jar lids with their flower surrounds on the feeding station.

5 Carefully pour **sugar solution** into each jam-jar lid.

6 Your **butterfly feeder** is ready for its first diners!

TOP TIP!

To welcome more **caterpillars** and **butterflies** into your garden, you could try growing things they are attracted to, like **nasturtium plants** with their **red and orange flowers**.

TOP TIP!

Instead of making your own flowers from card, you could cut out **photos of flowers from a gardening magazine**.

MEET MISS SPIDER

'And here we have **Miss Spider**
With a mile of thread inside her
Who has personally
requested me to say
That she's **NEVER** met MISS MUFFET
On her charming little tuffet –
If she had she'd **NOT** have
frightened her away.
Should her looks sometimes alarm you
Then I don't think it would harm you
To repeat at least **A HUNDRED TIMES** a day:
"I must **NEVER** kill a spider
I must only **HELP** and **GUIDE** her
And invite her in the nursery to play."'

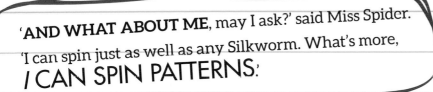

'**AND WHAT ABOUT ME**, may I ask?' said Miss Spider. 'I can spin just as well as any Silkworm. What's more, *I* CAN SPIN PATTERNS.'

'I do hope you'll find it **COMFORTABLE**,' Miss Spider said to the Old-Green-Grasshopper. 'I made it as SOFT and SILKY as I possibly could. I spun it with gossamer. That's a much better quality thread than the one I use for my own web.'

'Isn't it glorious!' Miss Spider said, coming over to join them. 'Personally, I had always thought that a BIG, **JUICY**, caught-in-the-web bluebottle was the finest dinner in the world – until I tasted *this*.'

. . . there was an **ENORMOUS** SPIDER . . . squatting upon a MAGNIFICENT chair.

I SPY-DER WITH MY LITTLE EYE . . .

James told the people of **New York** that they must vow **never to kill a spider**, and here are just a few reasons why!

DID YOU KNOW?

Spiders aren't actually insects at all. They are minibeasts with eight legs and are called **arachnids**. Their bodies comprise two parts and they have up to eight eyes!

HIDE-AND-SEEK

Spiders like to **hide in dark, quiet places**.

BABY SPIDERS

Female spiders wrap their eggs in something called an egg sac made from their silk. This helps to keep the eggs protected until they are ready to hatch.

BOTTOMS UP!

A spider's web is made of **silk that it pulls out of its bottom**!

KING OF THE SWINGERS

Spiders also use their silk to **swing through the air**.

SCARY

Spiders are often as afraid of you as you are of them, so you might see them run away if you get too close.

AAAAAAH!

NOT SO SCARY

Fear of spiders is known as **arachnophobia**. However, most spiders are harmless to humans. In fact, they are actually quite helpful because they **catch pesky flies**!

TUNNEL FUNNEL

Funnel spiders don't create flat webs; instead they weave themselves tunnels made of their silk.

DID YOU KNOW?

Spiders' webs are sticky, and when other minibeasts land on them they often can't wriggle free – just like the bluebottle that Miss Spider mentions!

53

WEAVE A WEB

Miss Spider made a **beautiful web** for herself across the corner of the room. Why don't you have a go at **weaving your own web** and **making a spider** to go on it?

DIFFICULTY RATING:

WHAT YOU WILL NEED:
- 60CM-SQUARE COLOURED THIN CARD
- 50CM-SQUARE WOODEN BOARD
- STICKY TAPE
- 12 DRAWING PINS
- KEY RING
- 4M FLAT WOVEN ELASTIC, ABOUT 5MM WIDE
- SCISSORS
- 10M THIN ELASTIC THREAD
- 4 BLACK PIPE CLEANERS
- BLACK AND ORANGE PONY BEADS

1

Fold the card over one side of the wooden board and secure underneath with sticky tape. Flip the board back over so that the side covered with card is facing upwards and **place the drawing pins around the edge of the board so that they are equally spaced**. Ask a grown-up for help with this.

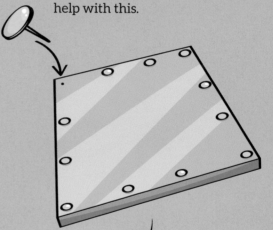

TOP TIP!

Instead of a key ring, you could use a **small ring** or **narrow washer**.

2

Place the key ring in the centre of the board. Then take the flat elastic and tie one end to one of the drawing pins. While **holding the key ring in position in the centre**, loop the other end of the flat elastic through the key ring, and **tie it to the drawing pin to the right of the first one**, then cut the thread.

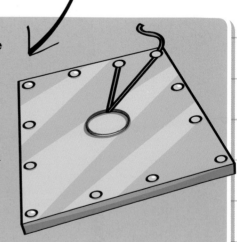

3 Repeat this for the **drawing pins directly opposite** (this will help to keep the key ring in position). Carry on until there are **six Vs of elastic** joining the drawing pins to the central key ring.

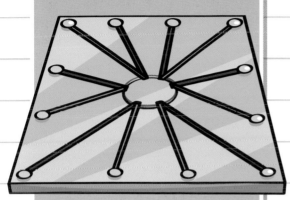

4 **Starting at the centre** and working towards the edge, tie one end of the thin elastic thread to the key ring and then make a spiral, **winding it around the flat elastic every time you come to a piece**. When you have reached the outside, **tie the thin elastic to a drawing pin** and cut off any remaining thread.

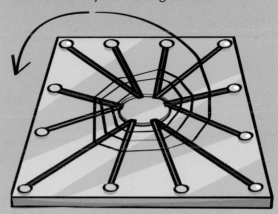

5 To make the spider, first gather the **pipe cleaners into a bunch and fold in half. Twist the section near the fold** several times – this is your spider's body. **Separate your spider's legs out** so that there are four on each side, just like Miss Spider has!

6 **Slide one black and one orange bead on to each leg** and push them up to the body. Next, **bend each leg up about 2 centimetres from the body** and slide on another black and another orange bead about **3 centimetres from the previous bend**, and then thread on another black and another orange bead. Your spider is complete and ready to sit on your newly spun web!

SUPER SPIDERS!

After eating the small green things, **Miss Spider** grew much larger. Although spiders don't get to quite her size, here are two that grow **quite big** . . .

THE GOLIATH BIRDEATER

This is a type of **tarantula** that prowls the forest floor in **South America**, feasting on not just insects but also worms, frogs, small reptiles and rodents. It has a **leg span of about 28 centimetres**, which is as long as this page! It weighs in at about **170 grams and can live for up to 25 years**!

THE GIANT HUNTSMAN SPIDER

Found in south-east Asia, this is the **widest** spider, measuring up to an incredible **30 centimetres! It was only discovered in 2001**, which means it must be pretty good at hiding.

A-MAZE-ING MISS SPIDER

Miss Spider was very proud of the **beds she spun** and the beautiful patterns she could create. But can you **find** your way through this **maze to the centre of the web?**

(Answer on page 83.)

START

57

BRILLIANT BEES

The **Old-Green-Grasshopper** was able to make **beautiful music** in the Giant Peach, but there's another **insect** whose sound creates a certain **buzz** . . .

LET'S BEE FRIENDS
Both honeybees and bumblebees are known as **'social'** bees because they live in groups in hives.

LEAVE ME ALONE
Some bees, including the **mining bee**, live on their own and are called **solitary bees**.

DID YOU KNOW?
There are nearly **20,000** known species of bee in **seven** recognized biological families.

BUZZ OFF!
A bee's buzz isn't produced by its **wings** but by **vibrating muscles**!

WOW!
Bees collect **pollen** from flowers in **pollen baskets** on their bodies!

LITTLE HELPERS
Bees are thought to be **very important to the survival of the human race**. It is estimated that a **third of all the food we eat** is dependent on pollination by bees.

SHOW ME THE HONEY!
Honey is made from the **nectar that bees collect from plants**. They store the honey in **honeycombs** and use it to feed the colony.

SUGAR POWER
If you see a bee on the ground looking a bit **sleepy**, it might need a sugar boost. **Dissolve some sugar in water on a teaspoon** and carefully offer it to the bee. It will use its tongue to drink the sugar solution, giving it enough energy to buzz off.

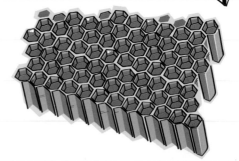

WICKED WASPS

Bees aren't the only insects you'll find **buzzing** around in the **summer months**; you might also come across **wasps**. They have a pretty **bad reputation**, but should we show them a little more love?

DID YOU KNOW?
There are over **100,000 species of wasp**, including the common wasp and the hornet.

WOW!
Common wasps like to **nest in hollows in trees** or even buildings. The nest gets bigger and bigger as more wasps live there, housing anything from **5,000 to 10,000 individuals**!

COOL!
Wasps make their nests from paper. They chew up wood and then spit it out as paper!

AHOY THERE!
Common wasps have an anchor-shaped marking on their faces.

GARDEN HELPERS
Wasps might not be high on the list of people's favourite insects, but they are good for gardens and parks – **they eat pests and help pollinate plants**.

HUGE HORNET
The **Asian giant hornet** is found in eastern Asia and has a wingspan of 7.5 centimetres and a body length of 4.5 centimetres!

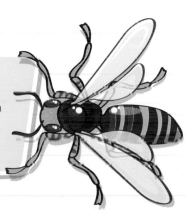

BUMBLEBEE FLOWERPOT HOUSE

The **Giant Peach** made a very unusual home for James and his friends! In fact, many **minibeasts** are drawn to **unusual places** to live. **Bumblebees**, for example, don't like living in houses made of bricks and mortar; they'd much prefer this fabulous **Flowerpot House**!

DIFFICULTY RATING: 🍎🍎🍎🍎🍏

WHAT YOU WILL NEED:

- SPADE OR TROWEL
- 30CM LENGTH OF HOSEPIPE
- TERRACOTTA FLOWERPOT, 22–24CM IN DIAMETER
- STRAW
- HAMSTER BEDDING OR COTTON WOOL
- PIECE OF SLATE OR AN OLD TILE

1

Find a suitable spot on a lawn and dig out a square that's about **20 centimetres square, and about 10 centimetres deep**. Make sure you get permission from whoever owns the lawn and ask a grown-up to help you.

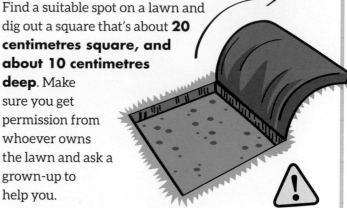

2

Place the hosepipe in a U shape in the hole. You may need to ask a grown-up to help you cut the hosepipe.

3

Cover the **hosepipe with the turf that you cut from the lawn**, leaving each end poking out – this is going to be a **tunnel** for your bumblebees!

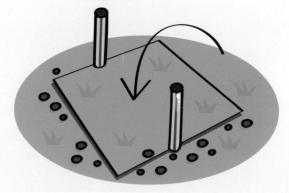

4

Fill the flowerpot with a mixture of **straw and hamster bedding** – this where your bumblebees nest.

5

Carefully turn the flowerpot upside down, making sure not to allow the straw and hamster bedding to fall out, and place it over one end of the hosepipe. The other end is going to be the bumblebees' entrance to their new home.

6

Use the **slate or old tile to cover the hole in the bottom of the flowerpot**, which will now be facing upwards. This stops any water getting into the bumblebees' home and keeps it nice and dry.

TOP TIP!

To **attract bumblebees** to your garden try planting things they like, including **lavender**, **shrub roses** and **hebe**.

MEET THE
GLOW-WORM

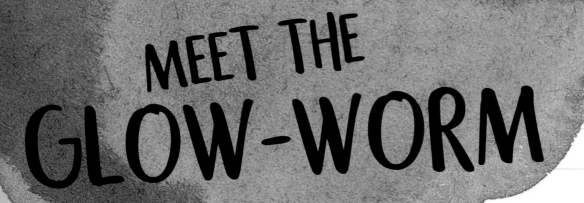

'AND NOW WITHOUT EXCUSE
  I'd like to introduce
This charming **GLOW-WORM**, lover of **SIMPLICITY**.
  She is easy to install
On your ceiling or your wall,
  And although this smacks a bit of **ECCENTRICITY**,
It's really rather clever
  For thereafter you will never
  You will **NEVER NEVER NEVER**
    Have the slightest need for using **ELECTRICITY**.'

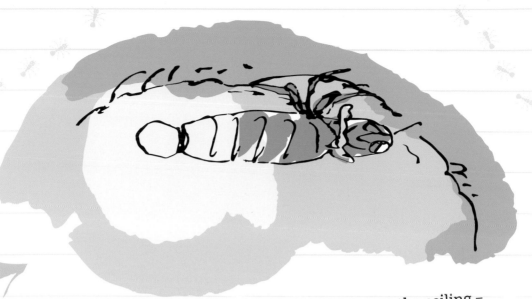

For the first time since entering the room, James glanced up at the ceiling – and there he saw a most extraordinary sight. Something that looked like a **GIGANTIC** FLY without wings (it was at least three feet long) was standing **UPSIDE DOWN** upon its six legs in the middle of the ceiling, and the TAIL END of this creature seemed to be literally on fire. A brilliant greenish light as bright as the **BRIGHTEST ELECTRIC BULB** was shining out of its tail and lighting up the whole room.

'It's a **GLOW-WORM**,' the Centipede answered. 'At least that's what *she* calls herself. Although actually you are quite right. She isn't really a worm at all. Glow-worms are NEVER WORMS. They are simply **LADY FIREFLIES WITHOUT WINGS**.'

Then a faint **GREENISH LIGHT** began to **glimmer** out of the Glow-worm's tail, and this gradually became stronger and stronger until it was enough to see by.

GLORIOUS GLOW-WORMS

The **Glow-worm** was able to provide **light** inside the Giant Peach, but how did she do this? Are there really **minibeasts** that can **glow**? Let's find out!

WHAT IS IT?
Although they are called glow-worms, they are actually **insects**.

SUMMER FUN
The story of *James and the Giant Peach* must have been set in the summer because the best time to spot glow-worms in Great Britain is on **warm evenings in June and July**. However, you don't just find them here – there are different species of glow-worm and firefly all around the world.

TURN ON THE LIGHTS!

Glow-worm beetles use a **chemical reaction** called bioluminescence to create their glow. Inside their bodies, they mix a compound called **luciferin with oxygen**, helped by an enzyme called **luciferase**.

WOW!

It isn't only glow-worms and fireflies that use **bioluminescence to create light**; other creatures do too, including **lanternfish, scaly dragonfish** and a type of octopus called the **glowing sucker octopus**.

LADY LIGHT

Male glow-worm beetles look like ordinary beetles with hard wing cases. However, the flightless female has a more flattened body and can indeed produce a greenish-yellow glow from her body.

GLOW-WORM WRISTBAND

James was amazed when he first noticed the **Glow-worm** hanging from the ceiling, providing **light inside the Giant Peach**. Your friends will be just as impressed with this easy-to-make **Glow-worm Wristband**.

DIFFICULTY RATING:

WHAT YOU WILL NEED:

- GREEN FELT
- PEN OR PENCIL
- SCISSORS
- PVA GLUE
- 2 GOOGLY EYES
- SILVER PIPE CLEANER
- GLOW STICK WITH CONNECTORS
- ELECTRICAL TAPE

1 **Draw a circle on the felt about 3 centimetres in diameter**; this is going to be your glow-worm's face. Then carefully cut it out using scissors – you might need to ask a grown-up to help you with this.

2 **Place two small blobs of PVA glue** on the felt face, place a **googly eye** on each one, and then set aside to dry.

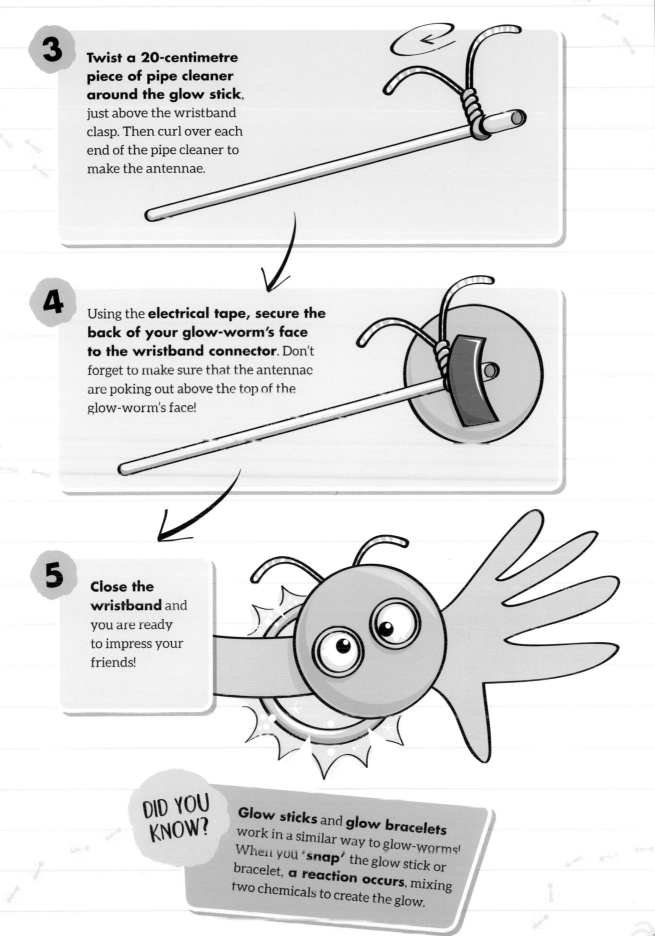

3 **Twist a 20-centimetre piece of pipe cleaner around the glow stick**, just above the wristband clasp. Then curl over each end of the pipe cleaner to make the antennae.

4 Using the **electrical tape, secure the back of your glow-worm's face to the wristband connector**. Don't forget to make sure that the antennae are poking out above the top of the glow-worm's face!

5 **Close the wristband** and you are ready to impress your friends!

DID YOU KNOW?

Glow sticks and **glow bracelets** work in a similar way to glow-worms! When you **'snap'** the glow stick or bracelet, **a reaction occurs**, mixing two chemicals to create the glow.

FANTASTIC FIREFLIES

James was keen to tell the people of **New York** about the the **Glow-worm's** usefulness, but there's another glowing insect that might make an even better light. **Meet . . . the firefly!**

DID YOU KNOW?
In **most species, both male and female** fireflies have the ability to **create light**.

NO-FLY ZONE
Just as a glow-worm isn't a worm, a **firefly isn't a fly**! It's a type of **beetle**.

FLASHLIGHT
Fireflies use their glowing bodies to **'talk' to their friends**, just like you might use a torch to communicate with your friends in the dark!

FLICK OF A SWITCH
Just like glow-worms, **fireflies** use **bioluminescence**. However, they have better control over their oxygen supply and can **switch their light on and off in an instant**, whereas it takes glow-worm beetles a few minutes.

WOW!
There are over **2,000 species** of firefly worldwide.

SHADOW SHAPES

The **Glow-worm's green light** was enough to fill the whole room, but can you work out **which insect is missing** in the **shadow** below? Is it the **Centipede**, the **Earthworm**, the **Silkworm**, the **Ladybird**, the **Grasshopper** or the **Spider**?

(Answer on page 83.)

MEET THE SILKWORM

'And now, the **Silkworm**,' James went on,
'Whose **SILK** will bear comparison
With all the greatest silks there are
In **ROME** and **PHILADELPHIA**.
If you would search the whole world through
From **PARAGUAY** to **TIMBUCTOO**
I don't think you would find one bit
Of silk that could compare with it.
Even the shops in **SINGAPORE**
Don't have the stuff. And what is more,
This Silkworm had, I'll have you know,
The honour, not so long ago,
To **spin** and **weave** and **sew** and **press**
The **QUEEN OF ENGLAND'S** wedding dress.
And she's already made and sent
A waistcoat for your **PRESIDENT**.'

On the floor over in the far corner, there was something **THICK** and **WHITE** that looked as though it might be a **Silkworm**. But it was sleeping soundly and nobody was paying any attention to it.

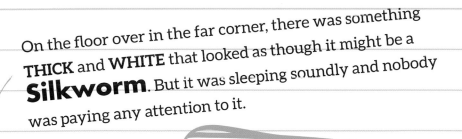

'**THE SILKWORM!**' cried the Old-Green-Grasshopper. 'Didn't you ever notice the Silkworm? She's still downstairs! She never moves! She just lies there **SLEEPING ALL DAY LONG**, but we can easily wake her up and make her spin!'

At the same time, up went **James's** hand and the **SEAGULL** flew right into the loop of silk that he was holding out. The loop, which had been cleverly made, tightened just the right amount (but not too much) around its neck, and the SEAGULL WAS CAPTURED.

SUPERSTAR SILKWORMS

James boasted that the **Silkworm** had created the **Queen of England's wedding dress** and made a **waistcoat** for the **President of the United States**. Are there really minibeasts capable of making silk that can be used to create clothes? Read on to find out.

DID YOU KNOW?

Silkworms aren't worms at all but are actually the **larvae or caterpillars of the silk moth**.

HEAVYWEIGHT CHAMPION

A silkworm **multiplies its weight by about 10,000** from the moment it's born to when it creates its cocoon.

AMAZING!

If they wanted to fly anywhere, silk moths would have to **hitch a ride** on the seagull-propelled Giant Peach, because although they have wings **they aren't capable of flight**.

COOL COCOONS!

Silkworms work very hard **building their cocoons for about two days continuously**. Each cocoon contains a single unbroken thread of silk that measures almost 1 kilometre! It takes about **3,000 cocoons to produce 500 grams of silk**.

WOW!

Apart from bees, silkworms are the only insects to have been **domesticated and farmed by humans**. Silkworm farming began in China over 5,000 years ago.

SUPER SILKY

Individual silk threads are very thin. It can actually take up to **ten of these threads wound together to make 'reeled silk'**, which can then be used to make things like clothes and sheets.

HUNGRY WORK

Mulberry leaves are silkworms' favourite food. In the farms where they live, they are fed a constant supply of chopped mulberry leaves.

STICKY SITUATION

James took a while to **spot the Glow-worm** hanging from the ceiling, but he'd probably have had even more trouble spotting the insect world's **master of disguise**: the **stick insect**!

PHANTASTIC PHASMATODEA PHAMILY

Stick insects belong to the **phasmatodea family** and possess **fantastic camouflage** capabilities to protect themselves from predators. There are some members of the family that look like leaves and are called – you've guessed it – **leaf insects**!

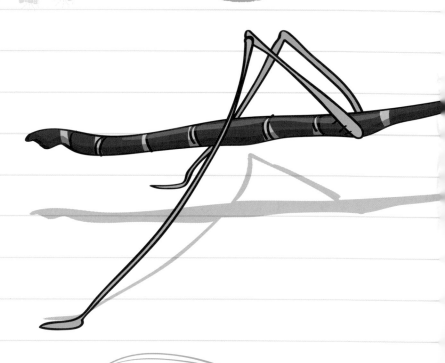

NEW CLOTHES

As they grow into adults, stick insects **shed their skin regularly** until they reach their full size.

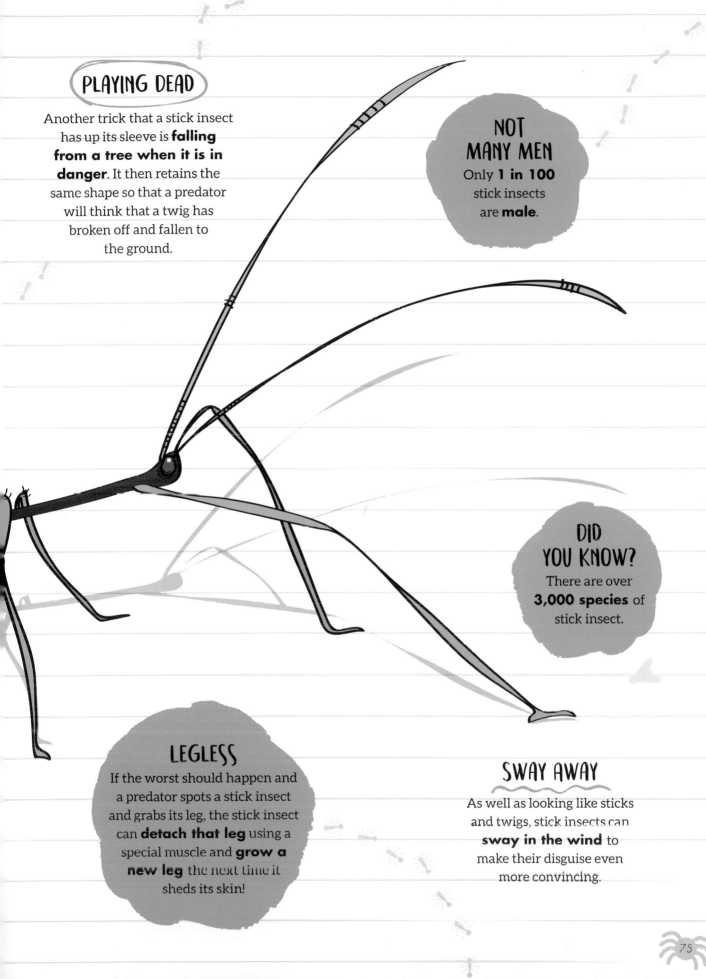

PLAYING DEAD

Another trick that a stick insect has up its sleeve is **falling from a tree when it is in danger**. It then retains the same shape so that a predator will think that a twig has broken off and fallen to the ground.

NOT MANY MEN

Only **1 in 100** stick insects are **male**.

DID YOU KNOW?

There are over **3,000 species** of stick insect.

LEGLESS

If the worst should happen and a predator spots a stick insect and grabs its leg, the stick insect can **detach that leg** using a special muscle and **grow a new leg** the next time it sheds its skin!

SWAY AWAY

As well as looking like sticks and twigs, stick insects can **sway in the wind** to make their disguise even more convincing.

TRICK STICK

James managed to outwit **Aunt Sponge** and **Aunt Spiker** when he escaped and made **friends** with all the bugs in the Giant Peach. Here's a way for you to get **one over** on your family and friends and **trick them** into thinking you've got a **new pet**!

DIFFICULTY RATING:

WHAT YOU WILL NEED:

- PLASTIC AQUARIUM
- OLD LEAVES
- BRANCH THAT WILL FIT INSIDE THE AQUARIUM
- SOME ROCKS
- SMALL PLASTIC BOWL FILLED WITH WATER
- VARIETY OF SMALLER STICKS AND TWIGS

TOP TIP!
If you can't get hold of an aquarium, you could use an **old ice-cream tub** or other plastic box.

1 **Scatter some old leaves** inside the aquarium so that the floor is covered.

2 Prepare the habitat for your stick insect by placing a **large branch in the aquarium**. Then put some rocks on the leaves, and finally the plastic bowl filled with water.

3 **This is the most important step**: you need to select a stick or a twig that looks like it could be an insect. You'll need one that has a thicker 'body' that's about **10 centimetres long, with a knobbly 'head' and some thinner 'legs'** coming out of the side. If necessary, you might need to trim or break some bits off to achieve the ideal stick-insect shape.

4 Place your **'stick insect'** on the branch inside the aquarium and invite your family and friends to come and meet your new pet! Make sure that you explain that it is very shy and doesn't move when it senses **potential predators** (like humans) nearby!

TOP TIP! When you are sure that no one is watching, you can **reposition your stick insect** and then call your family and friends back to see that it has moved!

BUG SAFARI

Tania and the Heads went on an adventure across the seas and ended up in **New York City**. However, you don't have to travel quite that far to go on your own **bug safari**. You could look in your **garden**, a **local park**, some **woodland** or even your **school playground**. If you are somewhere public make sure if you **ask permission** before...

...like a portable...

...how many...

...track the...

...date and location!

BUMBLEBEE

DATE SPOTTED: ....

LOCATION: ....

LADYBIRD

DATE SPOTTED: ....

LOCATION: ....

WOODLOUSE

DATE SPOTTED: ....

LOCATION: ....

EARTHWORM

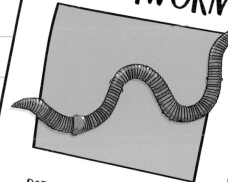

DATE SPOTTED: ....

LOCATION: ....

SPIDER

DATE SPOTTED: ....

LOCATION: ....

CENTIPEDE

DATE SPOTTED: ....

LOCATION: ....

GRASSHOPPER

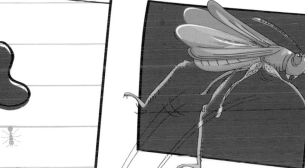

DATE SPOTTED: ....

LOCATION: ....

FIELD NOTES

When **James** and his friends first arrived in **New York**, the locals wondered whether there was a **Wampus** among them, or perhaps a **Gorgon** or an **Oinck**, possibly a **Cockatrice**, or even a **giant Scorpula**.

You might come across **bugs that you don't know** the name of on your travels. Why not **sketch them on these pages** and do some **research** to see if you can **identify them?** And if you can't, you could **make up names** for them yourself – like the ones above!

INSECT OPAEDIA

Abdomen The rear section of an insect's body

Antenna One of two feelers on an insect's head, used for smelling and touching

Arachnophobia A fear of spiders

Clitellum A worm's saddle containing maturing eggs

Entomologist A scientist with a special interest in insects

Entomophobia A fear of insects – also known as insectophobia

Exoskeleton The insect's skeleton – unlike humans, insects have their skeleton on the outside of the body, providing extra protection

Mandible The jaw of an insect

Proboscis A special type of insect tongue with a hollow tube for sucking up liquid foods like nectar

Radula The mouth of molluscs, such as slugs and snails, which contains tiny 'teeth'

Social insects Insects that live together in groups, like some bees and ants

Thorax The middle section of an insect's body – an insect's legs and wings are joined to its thorax

ANSWERS

PAGE **9**

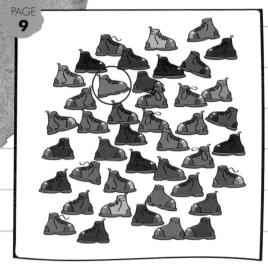

PAGE **21**

B

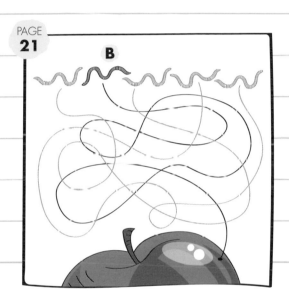

PAGE **33**

PAGE **45**

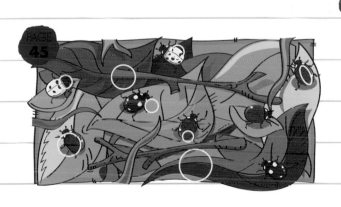

PAGE **57**

PAGE **69** The **Spider** is missing.

HOW MANY HAVE YOU READ?

   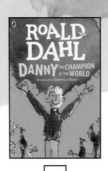 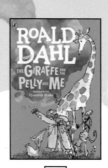 

☐ ☐ ☐ ☐ ☐ ☐

 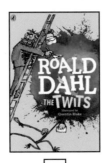    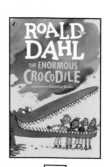

☐ ☐ ☐ ☐ ☐ ☐

 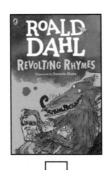   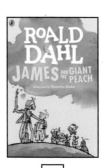

☐ ☐ ☐ ☐ ☐

FEWER THAN 5? WHOOPSY-SPLUNKERS! You've got some reading to do!

BETWEEN 5 AND 10? Wonderful surprises await! Keep reading . . .

MORE THAN 10? Whoopee! Which was your favourite?

ROALD DAHL DAY

CELEBRATE

THE **PHIZZ-WHIZZING**
WORLD of **ROALD DAHL**
EVERY YEAR on
13th SEPTEMBER!

JOIN THE PARTY AT
www.roalddahl.com

STORIES ARE GOOD FOR YOU.

Roald Dahl said,
*'If you have good thoughts, they will shine
out of your face like sunbeams and you
will always look lovely.'*

We believe in doing good things.
That's why ten per cent of all Roald Dahl income*
goes to our charity partners. We have supported
causes including: specialist children's nurses, grants for
families in need, and educational outreach programmes.
Thank you for helping us to sustain this vital work.

Find out more at roalddahl.com

The Roald Dahl Charitable Trust is a registered UK charity (no. 1119330).
* All author payments and royalty income net of third-party commissions.